We either find a way, or make a way.
—*General Hannibal*

How to Excel and Achieve Success

1. Know Thyself. Before you can do anything, and do it well enough to succeed, you must first know who you are and what you want. Know your strengths and weaknesses. Build on your strengths; work to improve your weaknesses.

2. Set Well-Defined Goals. Get definite about what you really want, define your goals, and then write them down in detail. It's easier to stay focused if you have a steady target to aim for.

3. Maintain your Focus, Keep your Drive. To excel, to succeed, you need to focus on your task—the planning, goal-setting, and managing of time. Block out distractions and continue striving toward your goals.

4. Never Give Up, Never Give In. Seeing a goal through to completion can be difficult, but those who excel, who truly succeed, never give up. They continue reaching for the brass ring, staying focused, and keeping an eye on the prize.

Goal Setting Strategies

When setting goals, start by getting definite about what you want then make plans on how to get there. These strategies can help:

1. Identify your life's purpose. What do you ultimately want out of this life? Before you can set goals for yourself, you have to know your life's purpose.

2. Make a list of short-and long-term goals. Review each one to make sure they support your life's purpose, and that they are truly something you want and not just something that sounds good.

3. Refine your goals to ensure all major life areas are being addressed. These life areas are: Family/Home, Career/Finances, Social Life/Culture, Spirituality/Ethics, Physical and Mental Health, and Education. If you are focusing on one area too much and another area not enough, adjust your goals so that your life is balanced.

4. Write down each goal in detail. Be specific about what you mean. If you want a career, tell what kind of career, in what field, doing what type of work, making what type of salary. Write down each goal in your journal so you can review it and track your progress.

5. Map out your path to success. For each goal listed in your journal, develop the steps you will need to take to reach it. Do some research. Ask questions. Don't short-change yourself here. Be thorough.

6. Track your progress. Periodically review your goals and the steps you mapped out to renew your focus. Make adjustments to your plans as needed. Write down the progress you have made, successes and failures, and continue striving toward your goals. Use self-talk to stay positive and remember, never give up.

Make no little **plans**; they have no magic to stir

men's blood...Make big plans; aim **high** in hope and work.

—*Daniel Hudson Burnham*

To accomplish great things,

in which you really stop to **look** fear in the face.
You must do the thing you **think** you cannot do.

—*Eleanor Roosevelt*

men's blood...Make big plans; aim **high** in hope and work.

—*Daniel Hudson Burnham*

To accomplish great things,

men's blood...Make big plans; aim **high** in hope and work.

—*Daniel Hudson Burnham*

To accomplish great things,

we must not only act, but also dream; not only plan, but also believe.

—Anatole France

You gain strength, courage, and **confidence** by every experience

men's blood...Make big plans; aim **high** in hope and work.

—*Daniel Hudson Burnham*

To accomplish great things,

we must not only act, but also dream; not only plan, but also believe.
—Anatole France

You gain strength, courage, and **confidence** by every experience

we must not only act, but also dream; not only plan, but also believe.

—Anatole France

in which you really stop to look fear in the face.
You must do the thing you think you cannot do.

—Eleanor Roosevelt

we must not only act, but also dream; not only plan, but also believe.

—Anatole France

You gain strength, courage, and confidence by every experience

in which you really stop to **look** fear in the face.
You must do the thing you **think** you cannot do.

—*Eleanor Roosevelt*

To accomplish great things, we must not only act, but also dream; not only plan, but also believe.

—Anatole France

You gain strength, courage, and **confidence** by every experience

men's blood...Make big plans; aim **high** in hope and work.

—*Daniel Hudson Burnham*

To accomplish great things,

men's blood...Make big plans; aim **high** in hope and work.

—*Daniel Hudson Burnham*

To accomplish great things,

in which you really stop to **look** fear in the face.
You must do the thing you **think** you cannot do.

—Eleanor Roosevelt

we must not only act, but also dream; not only plan, but also believe.

—*Anatole France*

You gain strength, courage, and **confidence** by every experience

men's blood...Make big plans; aim **high** in hope and work.

—*Daniel Hudson Burnham*

men's blood...Make big plans; aim high in hope and work.

—*Daniel Hudson Burnham*

To accomplish great things,

in which you really stop to **look** fear in the face.
You must do the thing you **think** you cannot do.

—*Eleanor Roosevelt*

in which you really stop to look fear in the face.
You must do the thing you think you cannot do.

—*Eleanor Roosevelt*

we must not only act, but also dream; not only plan, but also believe.

—Anatole France

we must not only act, but also dream; not only plan, but also believe.

—Anatole France

You gain strength, courage, and **confidence** by every experience

men's blood...Make big plans; aim **high** in hope and work.

—*Daniel Hudson Burnham*

To accomplish great things,

in which you really stop to look fear in the face.
You must do the thing you think you cannot do.

—*Eleanor Roosevelt*

we must not only act, but also dream; not only plan, but also believe.

—Anatole France

we must not only act, but also dream; not only plan, but also believe.

—Anatole France

You gain strength, courage, and **confidence** by every experience

men's blood...Make big plans; aim **high** in hope and work.

—*Daniel Hudson Burnham*

To accomplish great things,

we must not only act, but also dream; not only plan, but also believe.

—Anatole France

men's blood...Make big plans; aim **high** in hope and work.

—*Daniel Hudson Burnham*

To accomplish great things,

men's blood...Make big plans; aim high in hope and work.

—Daniel Hudson Burnham

To accomplish great things,

in which you really stop to **look** fear in the face.
You must do the thing you **think** you cannot do.

—*Eleanor Roosevelt*

Make no little **plans**; they have no magic to stir

we must not only act, but also dream; not only plan, but also believe.

—Anatole France

You gain strength, courage, and **confidence** by every experience

men's blood...Make big plans; aim **high** in hope and work.

—*Daniel Hudson Burnham*

To accomplish great things,

men's blood...Make big plans; aim high in hope and work.

—Daniel Hudson Burnham

To accomplish great things,

in which you really stop to **look** fear in the face.
You must do the thing you **think** you cannot do.

—*Eleanor Roosevelt*

Make no little **plans**; they have no magic to stir

in which you really stop to look fear in the face.
You must do the thing you think you cannot do.

—Eleanor Roosevelt

Make no little **plans**; they have no magic to stir

we must not only act, but also dream; not only plan, but also believe.

—Anatole France

You gain strength, courage, and **confidence** by every experience

we must not only act, but also dream; not only plan, but also believe.

—Anatole France

men's blood...Make big plans; aim **high** in hope and work.

—*Daniel Hudson Burnham*

To accomplish great things,

in which you really stop to look fear in the face.
You must do the thing you think you cannot do.

—Eleanor Roosevelt

we must not only act, but also dream; not only plan, but also believe.

—*Anatole France*

we must not only act, but also dream; not only plan, but also believe.

—*Anatole France*

men's blood...Make big plans; aim **high** in hope and work.

—Daniel Hudson Burnham

To accomplish great things,

we must not only act, but also dream; not only plan, but also believe.

—Anatole France

You gain strength, courage, and **confidence** by every experience

men's blood...Make big plans; aim **high** in hope and work.

—*Daniel Hudson Burnham*

To accomplish great things,

men's blood...Make big plans; aim **high** in hope and work.

—*Daniel Hudson Burnham*

To accomplish great things,

in which you really stop to **look** fear in the face.
You must do the thing you **think** you cannot do.

—*Eleanor Roosevelt*

we must not only act, but also dream; not only plan, but also believe.

—Anatole France

men's blood...Make big plans; aim **high** in hope and work.

To accomplish great things,

men's blood...Make big plans; aim **high** in hope and work.

—Daniel Hudson Burnham

To accomplish great things,

in which you really stop to **look** fear in the face.
You must do the thing you **think** you cannot do.

—*Eleanor Roosevelt*

in which you really stop to look fear in the face.
You must do the thing you think you cannot do.

—*Eleanor Roosevelt*

we must not only act, but also dream; not only plan, but also believe.

—Anatole France

we must not only act, but also dream; not only plan, but also believe.

—Anatole France

men's blood...Make big plans; aim **high** in hope and work.

—*Daniel Hudson Burnham*

To accomplish great things,

in which you really stop to look fear in the face.
You must do the thing you think you cannot do.

—*Eleanor Roosevelt*

we must not only act, but also dream; not only plan, but also believe.

—Anatole France

You gain strength, courage, and **confidence** by every experience

we must not only act, but also dream; not only plan, but also believe.

—Anatole France

men's blood...Make big plans; aim **high** in hope and work.

—Daniel Hudson Burnham

we must not only act, but also dream; not only plan, but also believe.

—Anatole France

men's blood...Make big plans; aim **high** in hope and work.

—Daniel Hudson Burnham

To accomplish great things,

men's blood...Make big plans; aim **high** in hope and work.

—*Daniel Hudson Burnham*

To accomplish great things,

in which you really stop to **look** fear in the face. You must do the thing you **think** you cannot do.

—*Eleanor Roosevelt*

we must not only act, but also dream; not only plan, but also believe.
—Anatole France

men's blood...Make big plans; aim **high** in hope and work.

—*Daniel Hudson Burnham*

To accomplish great things,

men's blood...Make big plans; aim **high** in hope and work.

—*Daniel Hudson Burnham*

To accomplish great things,

in which you really stop to **look** fear in the face.
You must do the thing you **think** you cannot do.

—*Eleanor Roosevelt*

in which you really stop to look fear in the face.
You must do the thing you think you cannot do.

—Eleanor Roosevelt

we must not only act, but also dream; not only plan, but also believe.

—Anatole France

You gain strength, courage, and **confidence** by every experience

we must not only act, but also dream; not only plan, but also believe.

—Anatole France

men's blood...Make big plans; aim **high** in hope and work.

—*Daniel Hudson Burnham*

To accomplish great things,

in which you really stop to look fear in the face.
You must do the thing you think you cannot do.

—Eleanor Roosevelt

Make no little **plans**; they have no magic to stir

we must not only act, but also dream; not only plan, but also believe.

—Anatole France

we must not only act, but also dream; not only plan, but also believe.

—*Anatole France*

men's blood...Make big plans; aim high in hope and work.

—Daniel Hudson Burnham

To accomplish great things,

we must not only act, but also dream; not only plan, but also believe.

—Anatole France

You gain strength, courage, and **confidence** by every experience

men's blood...Make big plans; aim **high** in hope and work.

—Daniel Hudson Burnham

To accomplish great things,

men's blood...Make big plans; aim high in hope and work.

—Daniel Hudson Burnham

To accomplish great things,

in which you really stop to **look** fear in the face.
You must do the thing you **think** you cannot do.

—*Eleanor Roosevelt*

Make no little **plans**; they have no magic to stir

we must not only act, but also dream; not only plan, but also believe.

—*Anatole France*

You gain strength, courage, and **confidence** by every experience

men's blood...Make big plans; aim **high** in hope and work.

—*Daniel Hudson Burnham*

To accomplish great things,

men's blood...Make big plans; aim **high** in hope and work.

—*Daniel Hudson Burnham*

To accomplish great things,

in which you really stop to **look** fear in the face.
You must do the thing you **think** you cannot do.

—*Eleanor Roosevelt*

Make no little **plans**; they have no magic to stir

in which you really stop to look fear in the face.
You must do the thing you think you cannot do.

—Eleanor Roosevelt

we must not only act, but also dream; not only plan, but also believe.

—Anatole France

we must not only act, but also dream; not only plan, but also believe.

—Anatole France

men's blood...Make big plans; aim **high** in hope and work.

—Daniel Hudson Burnham

To accomplish great things,

in which you really stop to look fear in the face.
You must do the thing you think you cannot do.

—*Eleanor Roosevelt*

we must not only act, but also dream; not only plan, but also believe.

—*Anatole France*

You gain strength, courage, and **confidence** by every experience

we must not only act, but also dream; not only plan, but also believe.

—Anatole France

men's blood...Make big plans; aim **high** in hope and work.

—Daniel Hudson Burnham

To accomplish great things,

we must not only act, but also dream; not only plan, but also believe.

—Anatole France

men's blood...Make big plans; aim **high** in hope and work.

—Daniel Hudson Burnham

To accomplish great things,

men's blood...Make big plans; aim **high** in hope and work.

—Daniel Hudson Burnham

To accomplish great things,

in which you really stop to **look** fear in the face.
You must do the thing you **think** you cannot do.

—*Eleanor Roosevelt*

Make no little **plans**; they have no magic to stir

in which you really stop to **look** fear in the face.
You must do the thing you **think** you cannot do.

—*Eleanor Roosevelt*

we must not only act, but also dream; not only plan, but also believe.

—Anatole France

You gain strength, courage, and **confidence** by every experience

we must not only act, but also dream; not only plan, but also believe.
—*Anatole France*

men's blood...Make big plans; aim high in hope and work.

—Daniel Hudson Burnham

To accomplish great things,

n which you really stop to **look** fear in the face.
You must do the thing you **think** you cannot do.

—*Eleanor Roosevelt*

men's blood...Make big plans; aim high in hope and work.

—Daniel Hudson Burnham

To accomplish great things,

in which you really stop to look fear in the face.
You must do the thing you think you cannot do.

—Eleanor Roosevelt

men's blood...Make big plans; aim **high** in hope and work.

—*Daniel Hudson Burnham*

To accomplish great things,

men's blood...Make big plans; aim **high** in hope and work.

—*Daniel Hudson Burnham*

To accomplish great things,

we must not only act, but also dream; not only plan, but also believe.

—Anatole France

You gain strength, courage, and **confidence** by every experience

men's blood...Make big plans; aim **high** in hope and work.

—*Daniel Hudson Burnham*

To accomplish great things,

we must not only act, but also dream; not only plan, but also believe.

—Anatole France

You gain strength, courage, and **confidence** by every experience

we must not only act, but also dream; not only plan, but also believe.

—Anatole France

You gain strength, courage, and **confidence** by every experience

in which you really stop to **look** fear in the face.
You must do the thing you **think** you cannot do.

—*Eleanor Roosevelt*

we must not only act, but also dream; not only plan, but also believe.

—Anatole France

You gain strength, courage, and **confidence** by every experience

in which you really stop to **look** fear in the face.
You must do the thing you **think** you cannot do.

—*Eleanor Roosevelt*

No bird soars too high if he **soars** with his own wings.
—*William Blake*

Do more than is required.
What is the distance between someone who achieves their
goals consistently and those who spend their lives
and careers merely following?
The extra mile.
—*Gary Ryan Blair*